A-Z

of

CLASSICAL
MUSIC

Henderson

Wise Publications
part of *The Music Sales Group*
London / New York / Paris / Sydney / Copenhagen / Berlin / Madrid / Tokyo

Published by
Wise Publications,
14-15 Berners Street, London, W1T 3LJ, UK.

Exclusive distributors:
Music Sales Limited,
Distribution Centre, Newmarket Road, Bury St Edmunds,
Suffolk, IP33 3YB, UK.

Music Sales Pty Limited,
Music Sales Pty Limited
20 Resolution Drive,
Caringbah, NSW 2229, Australia.

Order No. AM994180
ISBN 978-1-84772-604-9
This book © Copyright 2008 by Wise Publications,
a division of Music Sales Limited.

Compiled and edited by Jessica Williams.
Cover Design by Ruth Keating.

Printed in the EU.

Your Guarantee of Quality

As publishers, we strive to produce every book
to the highest commercial standards.

This book has been carefully designed to minimise awkward page
turns and to make playing from it a real pleasure. Particular care has
been given to specifying acid-free, neutral-sized paper made from pulps
which have not been elemental chlorine bleached.

This pulp is from farmed sustainable forests and
was produced with special regard for the environment.

Throughout, the printing and binding have been planned to ensure
a sturdy, attractive publication which should give years of enjoyment.

If your copy fails to meet our high standards, please inform us
and we will gladly replace it.

www.musicsales.com

Ave Maria

Composed by Franz Schubert

Adagio

Air On The G String

Composed by Johann Sebastian Bach

The Arrival of the Queen of Sheba

Composed by George Frideric Handel

Allegro

Barcarolle

(from 'The Tales Of Hoffmann')

Composed by Jacques Offenbach

Allegretto moderato

D.C. al Coda

⊕ Coda

The Birdcatcher's Song
(from 'The Magic Flute')

Composed by Wolfgang Amadeus Mozart

Andante

* The small notes indicate the original version which can be played instead of the simplified version if preferred.

Brandenburg Concerto No.6
(2nd Movement)

Composed by Johann Sebastian Bach

Adagio, ma non tanto

rit.

The Can Can
(from 'Orpheus In The Underworld')

Composed by Jacques Offenbach

Canon in D

Composed by Johann Pachelbel

Christmas Concerto
(3rd Movement: 'Pastorale')

Composed by Arcangelo Corelli

Clair de Lune

Composed by Claude Debussy

Andante très expressif

Dance Of The Blessed Spirits
(from 'Orfeo ed Euridice')

Composed by Christoph Willibald von Gluck

La Donna è Mobile

(from 'Rigoletto')

Composed by Giuseppe Verdi

Fine

D.C. al Fine

German Dance

('The Sleigh Ride')

Composed by Wolfgang Amadeus Mozart

Eine kleine Nachtmusik

(1st Movement)

Composed by Wolfgang Amadeus Mozart

Enigma Variations
(Theme)

Composed by Sir Edward Elgar

Etude No.3

Op.10

Composed by Frédéric Chopin

Flower Duet
(from 'Lakmé')

Composed by Leo Delibes

Andantino con moto

Für Elise

Composed by Ludwig van Beethoven

Andante con moto

Gymnopédie No.1

Composed by Erik Satie

Habañera
(from 'Carmen')

Composed by Georges Bizet

*♪♪♪ original rhythm
⌞ 3 ⌟

'Hallelujah' Chorus
(from 'Messiah')

Composed by George Frideric Handel

Allegro con spiritoso

Horn Concerto No.4
(3rd Movement)

Composed by Wolfgang Amadeus Mozart

Imperial March

Composed by Sir Edward Elgar

allargando

rit.

Italian Concerto

Composed by Johann Sebastian Bach

Impromptu No.3

Composed by Franz Schubert

Jesu, Joy Of Man's Desiring

Composed by Johann Sebastian Bach

'Jupiter' Symphony No.41
(3rd Movement)

Composed by Wolfgang Amadeus Mozart

'Land Of Hope And Glory'
(Pomp And Circumstance March No.1)

Composed by Sir Edward Elgar

Kyrie Eleison

(from 'Mass No.12')

Composed by Wolfgang Amadeus Mozart

Largo

Composed by Arcangelo Corelli

Liebesträume

Composed by Franz Liszt

— Romantic Period

Rubato

Moderato

A tempo

rit.

Little Prelude in C

Composed by Johann Sebastian Bach

Allegro moderato

Nocturne No.2
Op.9

Composed by Frédéric Chopin

Mazurka No.2
Op.67

Composed by Frédéric Chopin

Minuet in G

Composed by Johann Sebastian Bach

'Moonlight' Sonata
Op.27, No.2

Composed by Ludwig van Beethoven

91

Nimrod
(from 'Enigma Variations')

Composed by Sir Edward Elgar

O, for the Wings of a Dove

Composed by Felix Mendelssohn

Ode To Joy
(from 'Symphony No.9, 'Choral'')

Composed by Ludwig van Beethoven

Allegro

poco rit.

98

Panis Angelicus

Composed by César Franck

Moderately

rall. al fine

Pictures At An Exhibition
(Promenade)

Composed by Modest Mussorgsky

Allegro giusto, nel modo Russico, senza allegreza, ma poco sostenuto

Pie Jesu
(from 'Requiem, Op.48')

Composed by Gabriel Fauré

Quartet No.2 (String)
(3rd Movement Theme)

Composed by Alexander Borodin

'Raindrop' Prelude No.15
Op.28

Composed by Frédéric Chopin

Sostenuto

The Ride Of The Valkyries
(from 'Die Walküre')

Composed by Richard Wagner

The Swan
(from 'The Carnival Of The Animals')

Composed by Camille Saint-Saëns

Andantino grazioso

rit.

A tempo

Spring
(from 'The Four Seasons')

Composed by Antonio Vivaldi

'Scottish' Symphony No.3
(1st Movement)

Composed by Felix Mendelssohn

Allegro un poco agitato

Tempo primo

D.S. al Fine

Symphony No.5
(4th Movement: 'Adagietto')

Composed by Gustav Mahler

Toccata and Fugue

Composed by Johann Sebastian Bach

Träumerei

Composed by Robert Schumann

Trout Quintet
(4th Movement)

Composed by Franz Schubert

The Unfinished Symphony
(Theme)

Composed by Franz Schubert

Variations on
'Ah, Vous Dirai-je, Maman'

Composed by Wolfgang Amadeus Mozart

Violin Concerto No.1
(2nd Movement)

Composed by Max Bruch

Adagio ♩ = 64

Waltz
(from 'The Sleeping Beauty')

Composed by Peter Ilyich Tchaikovsky

Allegro (Tempo di valse)

When I Am Laid In Earth

(from 'Dido And Aeneas')

Composed by Henry Purcell

William Tell Overture

(Theme)

Composed by Gioacchino Rossini

Allegro vivace

Winter
(from 'The Four Seasons')

Composed by Antonio Vivaldi

151

Xerxes
(Largo)

Composed by George Frideric Handel

The Young Prince And The Princess

(from 'Sheherazade')

Composed by Nikolay Rimsky-Korsakov

Andantino

Zadok The Priest

Composed by George Frideric Handel

159

123456789